W9-AJC-985

G P S

A Guide to the Next Utility

by

Jeff Hurn

for

TRIMBLE NAVIGATION

First Published in the United States 1989 by

Trimble Navigation Ltd.
645 North Mary Avenue
P.O. Box 3642
Sunnyvale, CA 94088-3642

+1 (408) 481-8000
FAX +1 (408) 481-2000

C O N T E N T S

What is GPS?

The solution to an age old problem.

Probably right from the time man got up on his hind legs and started to wander around the earth he's been looking for some simple way to figure out where he was and where he was going.

It's such a basic problem you'd think we'd have come up with something that really works. But right up until today every system has had problems.

Early travelers probably just marked their trails with piles of stones. But that only works right around your own camp.   And what happens when snow falls or when rain washes out the markers?

When man started to explore the oceans, the problem got even worse because there was no place to pile up the stones. And no landmarks to refer to.   The only thing you could count on were the stars.

Unfortunately, the stars are so far away they look pretty much the same no matter where you are.   So the only way to use them is to make very careful measurements. And of course these measurements can only be made at night — and only on *clear* nights.

Even with the best instruments, celestial navigation can really only tell you approximately where you are, give or take maybe a mile. And sometimes that isn't good enough, especially when you are trying to find a harbor at night.

Modern man with all his electronic gadgetry has tried a few tricky new systems, but even they have their problems. If you're a sailor you've probably heard of LORAN and DECCA. They are a radio based system that's pretty good for coastal waters where there are LORAN and DECCA chains.

But they don't cover much of the rest of the earth and their accuracy varies depending on electrical interference and geographic variations. Another new system that uses satellites like GPS is called the Transit System or "Sat-Nav". Unfortunately, the satellites it uses are in very low orbit and there aren't very many of them, so you don't get a fix very often. And since the system is based on low frequency Doppler measurements, even small movements at the receiving end can cause significant errors in position.

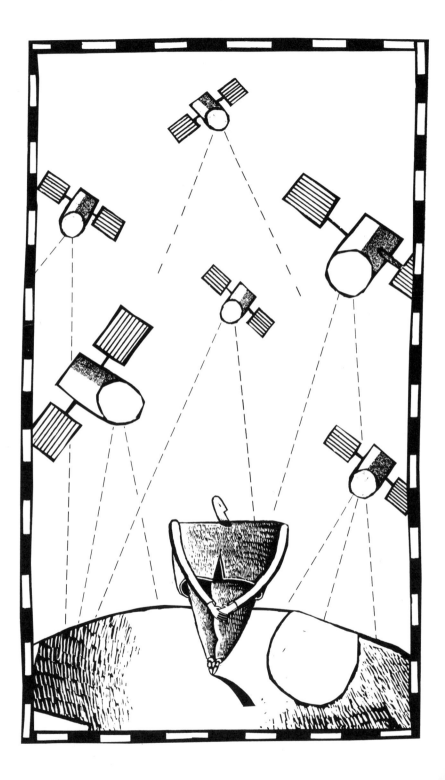

GPS - a global navigation system everyone can use.

_F_ inally, someone got fed up and said. "That's it! We 've got to have a system that works." That someone was the U.S. Department of Defense. They really need to know where things are and they've got the kind of money it takes to do the system right.

So they came up with something called the Global Positioning System or "GPS". It's based on a constellation of 24 satellites orbiting the earth at a very high altitude. In a way, you could think of them as "man-made stars" to replace the stars that we've traditionally used for navigation.

It's a massive undertaking. In fact, the U.S. government is investing over $12 billion to build the system. But it's money well spent because the system really works.

The satellites are high enough that they can avoid the problems encountered by land based systems and they use technology accurate enough to really give pinpoint positions anywhere in the world, 24 hours a day. In actual use, people are getting measurement accuracies better than the width of an average street. And in "differential" mode (more about this later) surveyors are using GPS to make measurements down to a centimeter.

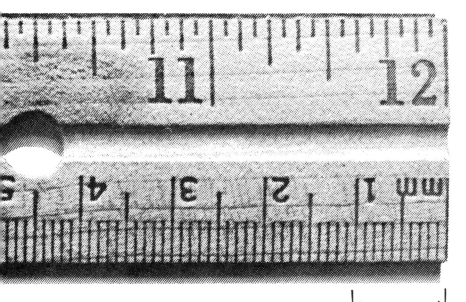

And since GPS was first and foremost a defense system, it's been designed to be impervious to jamming and interference. So we can expect it to be a very hardy system.

The new utility.   But what's most exciting
is its *potential.*   With today's integrated
circuit technology, GPS receivers are fast
becoming small enough and cheap enough to
be carried by just about anyone.   That means
that everyone will have the ability to know
exactly where they are, all the time.   Finally,
one of man's basic needs will be fulfilled.
This new service will become as basic as the
telephone.   Indeed, a "new utility."

The applications are almost limitless.
Some are obvious: Delivery vehicles will be
able to pinpoint destinations.   Emergency
vehicles will be more prompt.   And of course,
cars will have electronic maps that will instantly show us the way to any destination.
Other uses will follow. Since the system can
locate things in three dimensions it will work
for aircraft as well.   In fact, GPS is thought by
many to be the best (and cheapest) way to
design a fool-proof air collision avoidance
system.   And right now work is progressing on
very accurate zero-visibility landing systems.

Every place on earth will have a unique address. But that's just the start.

GPS really allows every square meter of the earth's surface to have a unique address. That means that whole new ways of organizing our work and play are possible. Imagine a future when the phone book is no longer a paper book but instead a computer database in the memory of your computer. And instead of just listing phone numbers and addresses the book also stores the exact GPS location of everything. Then when you're looking for a Chinese restaurant, your computer could search through the phone database, find the location nearest to your current location and direct you to it immediately. No more aimless hunting. No more wasted driving.

This new utility would give the world a new "international standard" for defining locations and distances and it would allow nations to monitor and use natural resources more efficiently than ever before.

Summary:

• Navigation has traditionally been an esoteric science.

• GPS was developed by the Department of Defense to simplify accurate navigation

• GPS uses satellites and computers to compute positions anywhere on earth. By the way, GPS has also been used on near earth satellites.

• Knowing where you are is so basic to life, GPS could become the next utility.

How GPS works.

In Five Easy Steps.

The basic principles behind GPS are really quite simple — even though the system itself employs some of the most "high-tech" equipment ever developed. To understand it, let's break the system into five conceptual pieces and take those pieces one step at a time. We'll start with the "big" ideas, and ignore some of the details. Then later, we'll fill in all the fine points.

To measure travel time, GPS needs very accurate clocks **3**

To triangulate, GPS measures distance using the travel time of a radio message **2**

G P S
In Five Easy Steps

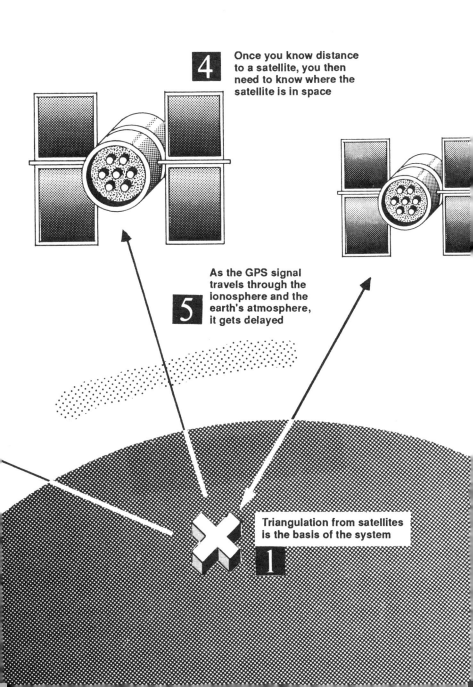

4 Once you know distance to a satellite, you then need to know where the satellite is in space

5 As the GPS signal travels through the ionosphere and the earth's atmosphere, it gets delayed

Triangulation from satellites is the basis of the system

1

The basic idea- Satellite ranging.

*G*PS is based on satellite ranging. That means that we figure
our position on earth by measuring
our distance from a group of satellites in
space.   The satellites act as precise reference
points for us.

You might ask: "How do we measure
exactly how far we are from a satellite way out
in space?   And how do we know exactly
where a moving satellite is?"   These are a
couple of the details we'll ignore for the
moment.   Trust me, they can be figured out.
Let's just assume for right now that we can
figure out exactly *where* a satellite is in space
and exactly *how far* we are from it.

Then the basic concept behind GPS is
simple: Let's say we're lost and we're trying
to locate ourselves.   If we know that we are a
certain distance from satellite A, say 11,000

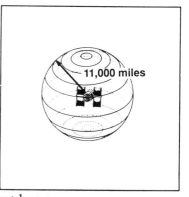

11,000 miles

miles, that really narrows down where in the whole universe we can be. It tells us we must be somewhere on an imaginary sphere that is centered on the satellite and that has a radius of 11,000 miles.

Now if at the same time we also know that we're 12,000 miles from another satellite, satellite B, that narrows down where we can be even more. Because the only place in the universe where we can be 11,000 miles from satellite A *and* 12,000 miles from satellite B is on the circle where those two spheres intersect.

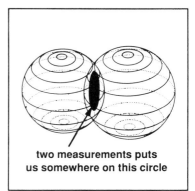

two measurements puts us somewhere on this circle

Then if we make a measurement from a third satellite we can really pinpoint ourselves. Because if we know that at the same time we're 13,000 miles from satellite C, there are *only two points* in space where that can be true. Those two points are where the 13,000 mile sphere cuts through the circle that's the intersection of the 11,000 mile sphere and the 12,000 mile sphere.

That's right. By ranging from three satellites we can narrow

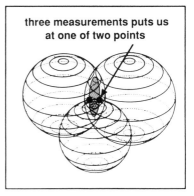

three measurements puts us at one of two points

down where we are to just *two* points in space.
(A little later we'll see that there's a technical
reason why we have to make another measurement — but for now, *theoretically,* three
measurements are enough).

How do we decide which one of those
two points is our true location? Well, we
could make a fourth measurement from another satellite. Or we can make an as-
sumption. Usually, one of the two points is a
ridiculous answer. The incorrect point may
not be close to the earth. Or it may have an
impossibly high velocity. The computers in
GPS receivers have various techniques for
distinguishing the correct point from the
incorrect one.

Incidentally, if you're sure of your
altitude, like mariners are (they know they're
at sea level), you can eliminate one of the
satellite measurements. One of the spheres in
our drawings can be replaced by a sphere
that's centered at the earth's center and has a
radius equal to your distance from the center
of the earth.

Anyway, if we wanted to be
absolutely technical, trigonometry says we
really need *four* satellite ranges to unambiguously locate ourselves. But in practice, we can

get by with just *three* if we reject the ridiculous solutions.

And that's it. The basic principle behind GPS: using satellites as reference points for triangulating your position somewhere on earth.

Everything else about the system is just technical details designed to help carry out this ranging process — to make it more accurate and easier to do. Now let's look at some of those details.

Summary:

• Position is calculated from distance measurements to satellites.

• Mathematically we need four measurements to determine exact position.

•Three measurements are enough if we reject ridiculous answers.

•Another measurement is required for technical reasons to be discussed later.

Measuring your distance from a satellite.

*S*ince GPS is based on knowing your distance to satellites in space, we need a method for figuring out how far we are from those satellites.

Surprisingly, the basic idea behind measuring a distance to a satellite is just the old "velocity times travel-time" equation we all learned in high school. You remember those word problems: "If a car goes 60 miles an hour for two hours, how far has it gone?" Well, it's **Velocity** (60 miles/hour) times travel **time** (2 hours) equals **distance** (120 miles).

The GPS system works by timing how long it takes a radio signal to reach us from a satellite and then calculating the distance from that time.

Radio waves travel at the speed of light: 186,000 miles per second. So if we can figure out exactly when the GPS satellite started sending its radio message and when we received it, we'll know how long it took to reach us. We just multiply that time in seconds by 186,000 miles per

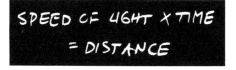

second and that's our range to the satellite. (And remember, all we need is three ranges to three different satellites and we've got our position).

Now of course, our clocks are going to have to be pretty good with short times because light moves awfully fast. In fact, if a GPS satellite were right overhead it would only take about 6/100ths of a second for the radio message to get to us.

So, in a way, GPS is a child of the electronic revolution. The kind of timing accuracy it demands is only possible because very precise electronic clocks are now relatively inexpensive. We're all familiar with those $20 quartz watches that keep unbelievable time. Well, GPS relies on an advanced form of that kind of timing. In fact most receivers can measure time with nanosecond accuracy. That's 0.000000001 second. We'll talk more about how they do it in a moment.

How do we know when the signal left the satellite? The big trick to measuring the travel time of the radio signal is to figure out exactly when the signal left the satellite. To do that the designers of the GPS system came up with a clever idea: Synchronize the satellites and receivers so they're generating the *same code* at exactly the *same time.* Then all we have to do is receive the codes from a satellite and then look back and see how long ago our receiver generated the same code. The time difference is how long the signal took to get down to us.

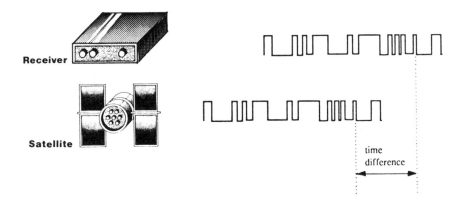

Receiver

Satellite

time difference

An everyday analogy To picture how this works, imagine you and a friend were standing at opposite ends of a football stadium. Now suppose there was a way to make sure that you both started counting to ten at exactly the same moment. And you both yelled the numbers out as you counted.

What you would hear at your end of the football stadium would be yourself saying: "One... two...three..." and then, a bit later, you'd hear your friend's voice saying "one... two..." and so on. You might already be up to "three" by the time you heard him saying "one." That's because it takes a while for the sound of his voice to get all the way across the stadium to you.

Since you both started yelling at the same time you could measure the time between when you said "one" and when you heard your friend say "one". That time would be the travel time for sound to cross the stadium. That's basically how the GPS system works.

The advantage of using a set of codes, or in the case of our analogy, a string of numbers, is that you can make the time measurement any time you want. You don't necessarily have to measure between when you said "one" and when you hear your friend say "one." You could do the same measurement between any pair of numbers, like when you say "eight" and when you hear your friend say "eight."—so you can jump in at any time.

Pseudo-random codes   The GPS system doesn't use numbers however. Both the satellites and the receivers actually generate a very complicated set of digital codes.

Pseudo-random code

The codes are made complicated on purpose so that they can be compared easily and unambiguously, and for some other technical reasons we'll talk about in a minute. Anyway, the codes are so complicated they almost look like a long string of random pulses.

They're not really random though, they're carefully chosen "pseudo-random" sequences that actually repeat every millisecond. So they're often referred to as the "pseudo-random" code.

Summary:

• The distance to a satellite is determined by measuring how long a radio signal takes to reach us from that satellite.

• We assume that both the satellite and our receiver are generating the same pseudo-random code at exactly the same time.

• We know how long it took for the satellite's signal to get to us by comparing how late its pseudo-random code is, compared to our code.

Getting perfect timing.

*B*ut wait a second (no pun intended). We know that light travels at 186,000 miles a second. If the satellite and our receiver were out of sync by even 1/100th of a second, our distance measurement could be off by 1,860 miles! How do we know both our receiver and the satellite are really generating their codes at exactly the same time?

Well, at least one side of the clock sync problem is easy to explain: the satellites have atomic clocks on board. They're unbelievably precise and unbelievably expensive. They cost about one hundred thousand dollars apiece and each satellite has four, just to be sure one is always working.

Atomic clocks don't run on atomic energy. They get the name because they use the oscillations of a particular atom as their

24

"metronome". It's the most stable and accurate time reference man has ever developed. So you can bet that when they think it's twelve noon, it's *exactly* twelve noon.

That's fine for the satellites, but what about us mortals down here on earth. If we had to have a hundred thousand dollar atomic clock in every GPS receiver only Donald Trump's yacht would have one.

Trigonometry to the rescue. Fortunately there's a way to get by with only moderately accurate clocks in our receivers — and the secret is to make an *extra* satellite range measurement. That's right — an extra distance measurement can make up for imperfect sync on our part. (Now you know why we were saying earlier that "*theoretically* three measurements are enough).

Trigonometry says that if three *perfect* measurements locate a point in 3-dimensional space, then four *imperfect* measurements can eliminate any timing offset (as long as the offset is consistent).

Now that may sound like a lot of technical mumbo-jumbo, but the idea is really pretty simple. And it's so fundamental to GPS that it's worth spending a little time to understand the principle.

The explanation will be a lot easier to understand with diagrams, and those diagrams will be a lot easier to draw if we work in just two dimensions. Of course GPS is a three dimensional system, but the principle we're discussing works the same in two dimensions. We just eliminate one measurement.

Why adding a measurement eliminates clock offset Here's how it works: Suppose our receiver's clock isn't perfect like an atomic clock. It's consistent like a quartz watch but it's not perfectly synced with universal time. Say it's a little fast, so that when it thinks it's twelve noon, it's really 11:59.59 AM. Let's look at what that would do to our position calculations.

Normally we'd talk about our "range" to a satellite in terms of miles or kilometers, but since those are just calculated from time, let's simplify things by talking about ranges as times. That way it'll be easier to see what clock errors can do to our position.

OK, let's say that, in reality, we're four seconds from satellite A and six seconds from satellite B. In *two* dimensions, those *two* ranges would be enough to locate us at a point. Let's call it "X" (Remember, it takes *three* measurements to locate a point in *three* dimensions).

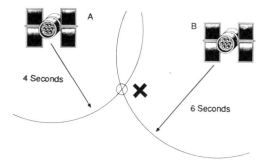

4 Seconds

6 Seconds

So "X" is where we *really* are and is the position we'd get if all the clocks were working perfectly. But now what if we used our "imperfect" receiver, which is a second fast? It would call the distance to satellite A, five seconds and the distance to satellite B, seven seconds. And that causes the two circles to intersect at a different point: "XX".

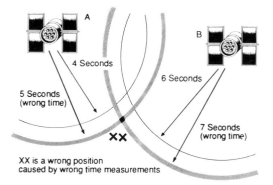

4 Seconds

6 Seconds

5 Seconds
(wrong time)

7 Seconds
(wrong time)

××

XX is a wrong position
caused by wrong time measurements

So XX is where our imperfect receiver would put us. And it would seem like a perfectly correct answer to us, since we'd have no way of knowing that our receiver was a little fast.

27

But it would be miles off. We'd probably notice something wasn't right when we started running into rocks, but nothing in the calculations would tell us.

Now this is where our trigonometry trick can help: Let's add another measurement to the calculation. In our two dimensional example, that means a third satellite.

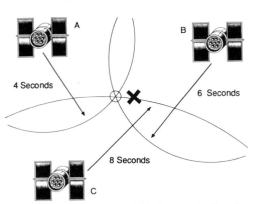

Let's say in reality (if we had perfect clocks) satellite C is eight seconds from our true position. The situation would look like the figure at the left.

Remember this drawing depicts the situation as it actually is.

All three circles intersect at X because those circles represent the true ranges to the three satellites.

Now let's add our one second offset to the drawing and see what happens. The dotted lines show the "pseudo-ranges" caused by our fast clock.   The phrase "pseudo-range" is used in GPS circles to describe ranges that contain errors (usually timing errors).
Notice that while A's and B's fast times still intersect at XX,   C's fast time is nowhere

near that point.   So there's no point that can really be five seconds from A, seven seconds from B and nine seconds from C.   There's no physical way those measurements can intersect.

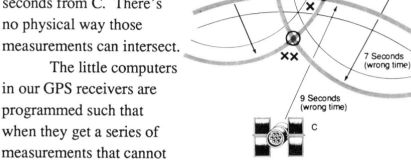

5 Seconds (wrong time)

7 Seconds (wrong time)

9 Seconds (wrong time)

The little computers in our GPS receivers are programmed such that when they get a series of measurements that cannot intersect at a single point, they realize something is wrong.   And they assume the cause is that their internal clock is off —that it has some offset.

So the computer starts subtracting (or adding) time, the same amount of time from all the measurements.   It keeps trimming off time from all the measurements until it hits on an answer that lets all the ranges go through one point. In essence, it "discovers" that by subtracting one second from all three measurements it can make the circles intersect at a point. And from this it assumes that its clock is one second fast.

Actually it doesn't really aimlessly hunt for an answer. The computers apply algebra to the problem. The old "four equations and four unknowns" exercise. And they quickly compute the clock offset. But the idea is the same: by adding one more measurement we can cancel out any consistent clock error our receivers might have.

Accurate 3-d measurements require four satellites In three dimensions this means that we really need to make *four* measurements to cancel out any error. And that's a very significant number to remember because it means that you can't get a truly accurate position until you have four satellites above the horizon around you.

The GPS system, when fully implemented, will consist of 24 satellites, so there will always be more than four visible from everywhere on earth. But right now, as the system is in its "formative years", there are times during the day when less than four satellites are overhead.

During these times, GPS can't do fully precise positioning. For this reason, some people are using receivers that integrate a GPS unit with another type of navigation system, like LORAN. The combination can provide "near-GPS" accuracy continuously because the GPS unit can be used, when the satellites are up, to establish a precise reference point for the LORAN. Then the LORAN can operate very accurately while the GPS satellites are below the horizon.

Needing four measurements affects receiver design. The need for four measurements has a big impact on the way GPS receivers are designed. We'll talk more about this in a separate chapter, but one very basic rule that comes out of all of this is that if you want continuous, real-time position measurements, you'll need a receiver with at least four channels. That is, one that can devote one channel to each of four satellites simultaneously.

Now many applications don't require that kind of instantaneous accuracy. For those a more economical single-channel receiver may suffice. A single channel receiver will have to sequence through four separate measurements to four different satellites before it can calculate an answer. The whole operation can take between 2 and 30 seconds, which for many applications is quite fast enough.

Unfortunately this type of receiver doesn't do as good a job monitoring velocity, which is one of the unique things about GPS: It can very accurately measure your speed. And any movement of the receiver while it's cycling through the four measurements can affect the accuracy of those measurements. Another disadvantage of the single-channel receiver shows up when the satellites transmit their "system data messages". These messages take 30 seconds to read, so navigation must be interrupted every time a new satellite is read.

A popular compromise is a three channel receiver. One channel performs the time measurement calculations while the other two establish a radio lock on the next satellite to be measured. When the first two channels have finished their time measurements, they can instantly switch to the new satellite without wasting any time "aquiring" it or listening to its condition message. The other channel, often called "housekeeping" channel, then looks ahead to the next satellite and begins the lock-on procedure for that one.

This can speed up the sequencing significantly, and with this system continuous position updates are always available. An added benefit is that the three channel set can be programmed to track up to eight satellites so that when one satellite is blocked, another can be instantly substituted without any interruption in the navigation process.

Summary:

•Accurate timing is key to measuring distance to satellites.

•Satellites are accurate because they have atomic clocks on board.

•Receiver clocks don't have to be perfect because a trigonometry trick can cancel out receiver clock errors.

•The trick is to make a fourth satellite range measurement.

•Needing four measurements affects receiver design.

Knowing where a satellite is in space.

We've been assuming, in all our discussions so far, that we know right where all the satellites are in space so we can triangulate our position from theirs. But how do we know where something that's 11,000 miles up in space, is?

A high satellite gathers no moss. Well, that 11,000 mile altitude is actually a benefit in this case. Something that high up is well clear of the earth's atmosphere. And that means that predictions of the satellites' orbits will be very accurate. Like the moon, which has reliably spun around this old planet for millions of years without any significant change in period, our GPS satellites are orbiting very predictably.

The Air Force injects each satellite into a very precise orbit according to the GPS master plan. The orbits are known in advance and, in fact, some GPS receivers on the ground have an "almanac" programmed into their computer's memory, which tells them where in the sky each satellite will be at any given moment.

All satellites are constantly monitored. Now this mathematical model of the orbits would be pretty accurate by itself, but, just to make things perfect, the GPS satellites are constantly monitored by the Department of Defense. That's one of the reasons the GPS satellites are not put into geo-synchronous orbit like TV satellites are. Since they go around the planet once every twelve hours, the GPS satellites pass over one of the DoD monitoring stations twice a day. This gives the DoD a chance to precisely measure their altitude, position and speed. The variations they're looking for are called "ephemeris" errors. They're usually very minor and are caused by things like gravitational pulls from the moon and sun and by the pressure of solar radiation on the satellite.

Once the DoD has measured a satellite's position, they relay that information back up to the satellite. Then that satellite will broadcast these minor corrections along with its timing information.

That's an important fact to remember: GPS satellites not only transmit a pseudo-random code for timing purposes but they also transmit a "data message" about their exact orbital location and their system's health. All serious GPS receivers use this information, along with the information in their internal almanacs, to precisely establish the position of the satellite.

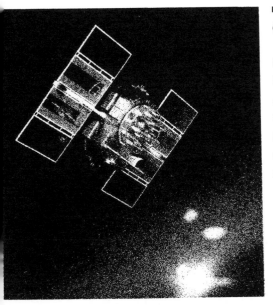

GPS Satellites

Name: NAVSTAR
Manufacturer: Rockwell International
Altitude: 10,900 nautical miles
Weight: 1900 lbs (in orbit)
Size: 17 ft with solar panels extended
Orbital Period: 12 hours
Orbital Plane: 55° to equatorial plane
Planned Lifespan: 7.5 years
Number built: 11 Block I prototype satellites 28 Block II production satellites
Constellation: 24 satellites

Summary:

•To calculate our position we not only need distance, we also need to know where our satellites are in space .

•GPS Satellites are so high up, their orbits are very predictable.

•Minor variations in orbits are measured constantly by the Department of Defense and that data is transmitted from the satellites themselves.

Ionospheric and atmospheric delays.

W e've seen that a lot of inge-
nuity has gone into ensuring
that every part of the GPS
system is as accurate as it can be. We've got
atomic clocks on the satellites and we use an
extra measurement to eliminate any error our
receiver clocks might have. The satellites even
broadcast up-to-the-minute corrections to their
orbital positions.   But as perfect as the system
seems to be, there are a couple of sources of
error that are very difficult to eliminate.

Perhaps the most significant of these
errors arises from the earth's ionosphere — a
blanket of electrically charged particles 80 to
120 miles above the earth. These particles
actually affect the speed of light and so affect
the speed of the GPS radio signals.   You may

be thinking: "Oh no, don't tell me there's a problem with the speed of light, that most sacred of all universal constants."

Well, the speed of light is only constant in a *vacuum*, like you might find in deep space. But when light (or a radio signal) goes through a denser medium, like a band of charged particles several miles thick, it slows down a bit. And that slowing will throw off our distance calculations because those calculations assume a constant speed of light.

Remember that car in the high school word problem? "How far does a car travel if it goes 60 miles an hour for 2 hours?" Well, imagine how difficult it would be to get the right answer if, somewhere along the way, the guy driving the car got out and bought a soda without telling us. That's kind of what light does. It slows down and speeds up depending on the medium it's traveling through.

There are a couple of ways we can try to minimize the error caused by this variation. For one thing, we can predict what the typical speed variation will be on an average day, under average ionospheric conditions, and then apply that correction factor to all our measurements. That will help, but unfortunately not every day is average.

Another way we can measure the variation in the speed of our signal is by looking at the relative speeds of two different signals. This starts to get into the realm of "esoteric physics" but the basic idea is this: When light travels through the ionosphere it slows down at a rate inversely proportional to its frequency squared. The lower the frequency of the signal, the more it gets slowed down.

So if we compare the arrival times of two different parts of the GPS signal, two parts that have different frequencies, we can deduce what kind of slowing they must have gone through. This kind of error correction is very sophisticated and is only found on the most advanced "dual-frequency" GPS receivers. It's called an "ionospheric-free solution" and with it, much of this kind of error can be eliminated.

After the GPS signals make it through the ionosphere, which is very high up, they enter the earth's atmosphere, where all our weather is. Unfortunately water vapor in the atmosphere can also affect the signals. The errors are similar in size to those caused by the ionosphere, but sadly this kind of error is almost impossible to correct. Fortunately, its net effect on our position calculations is considerably less than the width of the average street.

Ionospheric and atmospheric propagation delays are only one type of error that can creep into our measurements. So, since we're on the subject of inaccuracy, let's list all the things that can affect the ultimate accuracy of GPS.

As accurate as the atomic clocks on the satellites are, they're still subject to small variations. The DoD monitors these clocks and can adjust them when small deviations occur, but even so, slight inaccuracies can sometimes affect our measurements.

Like the atomic clocks in the satellites, our receivers on the ground sometimes make mistakes. The receiver may round off a mathematical operation or electrical interference might cause an erroneous correlation of the pseudo-random codes. These errors are usually very small or very big. It's easy to detect the big errors because they're so obvious, but it's sometimes difficult to discover small computational biases. These "receiver errors" can throw a few feet of uncertainty into every measurement.

Another type of error that really can't be blamed on the satellites or the receivers is "multipath error." It arises when the signals transmitted from the satellites bounce around before getting to our receiver. The result is that the signal doesn't go directly to the receiver as it should but instead takes a more circuitous path. It's the same effect that causes "ghosting" on TV. Modern receivers use advanced signal processing techniques and special antennae to minimize this problem, but in severe cases it can still add some uncertainty to a GPS measurement.

Errors mean uncertainty All of the sources of error we've discussed so far add together to give each GPS measurement a little uncertainty. Which means that instead of

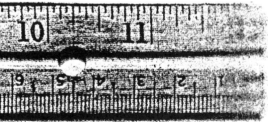

saying something is 10 feet away we have to say "it's 10 feet plus or minus a tenth of an inch." Or another way of looking at it is: your ruler doesn't have a sharp end, it has a fuzzy end.

Fortunately all of these inaccuracies taken together still don't add up to much of an error. In practice, GPS can tell you where you are to within probably a hundred feet — even better if you have a very good receiver.

Geometry — some angles are better than others. To get the best possible accuracy, a good GPS receiver will take into account a subtle principle of geometry called "Geometric Dilution of Precision".

Now, "Geometric Dilution of Precision" may sound like a lawyer's way of saying "we've got some errors here." But actually it refers to the fact that your solutions can be better or worse depending on which satellites you use to make a position measurement.

Not that one satellite is better than another. It's just that, depending on their relative angles in the sky, the geometry can magnify or lessen all the uncertainties we talked about before. It's a little like the pool player selecting a shot. He knows that with some angles on the balls he can be a little sloppy and still make the shot. Other angles magnify any slight mis-aim and make those low percentage shots.

To see how GDOP works let's look at our drawings again. We've been representing a satellite's range as a circle centered on the satellite. Well, now that we know that every measurement has a little uncertainty we should really represent the range as a "fuzzy" circle. Like the fuzzy end of the ruler, we can only say that our distance is something like 10,000 miles plus or minus .001 mile. So that means our drawings would look like this:

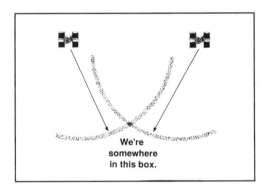

We're somewhere in this box.

The band is the area of uncertainty and so what we showed earlier as the *point* "X" is now really a little *box* called "X". Or in other words, the uncertainties mean that we can't say we're right on a single point, we can only say we're somewhere inside the area of the box.

Now here's what "Geometric Dilution of Precision" is all about. Depending on the angle between the satellites that little box can be nice and square and relatively small, or it could be very elongated and large.

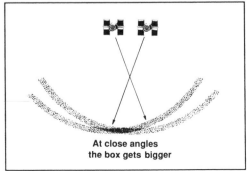

At close angles the box gets bigger

In simple terms, the wider the angle between satellites the better the measurement.

So, good receivers have computer routines which analyze the relative positions of all the satellites available and choose the four best candidates — those best positioned to reduce the size of the box. Even more sophisticated receivers compute your position based on all the satellites in view. That way the GDOP error is completely minimized.

GPS Accuracy

The ultimate accuracy of GPS is determined by the sum of several sources of error. The contribution of each source may vary depending on atmospheric and equipment conditions.

In addition, the accuracy of GPS can purposefully be degraded by the Department of Defense using an operational mode called "Selective Availability" or "S/A". S/A is designed to deny hostile forces the tactical advantage of GPS positioning. When, and if, it is implemented it will be the largest component of GPS error.

(cont.)

Error Budget
(as seen in real use by block 1 satellites)

Error Source (typical)

Satellite clock error	*2 feet*
Ephemeris error	*2 feet*
Receiver errors	*4 feet*
Atmospheric / ionospheric	*12 feet*
Worst case S/A (if implemented)	*25 feet*

Total (root -square sum)   15 to 30 feet
(depending on S/A *)*

To calculate the predicted accuracy, multiply the total above by the PDOP (Position Dilution of Precision).

PDOPs under good conditions range from 4 to 6. So the position accuracy that you can expect would be:

•Typical - good receiver	*60-100 feet*
•worst case	*200 feet*
•if S/A implemented	*350 feet*

Summary:

•The earth's ionosphere and atmosphere cause delays in the GPS signal that can translate into errors in position.

•Some of these errors can be eliminated with mathematics and modeling.

•Other sources of error are satellite clocks, our receivers, and multipath reception.

• Some configurations of satellites in the sky can magnify the other errors in the system.

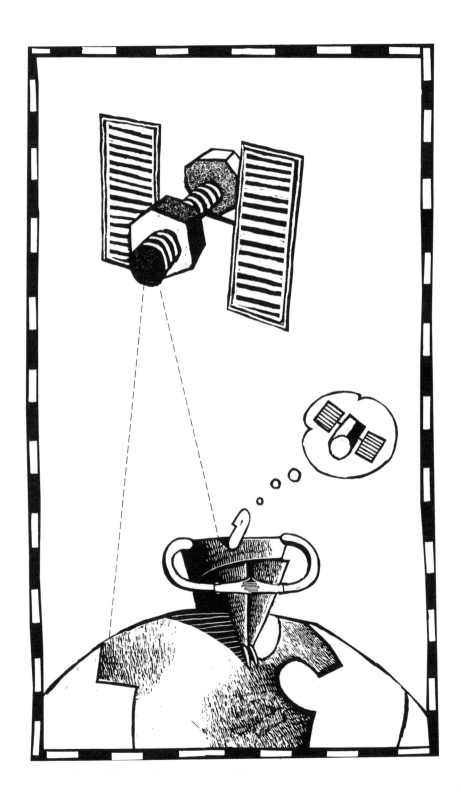

A few more
thoughts
for better
understanding.

*N*uts
and bolts,
high-flying concepts, and
down-to-earth tips.

→

6

Pseudo-random code
—the inside story.

*Y*ou may be asking yourself, "Why all this mumbo-jumbo about pseudo-random codes? Why not just send a normal radio signal like a satellite-TV signal?"

It's true — this pseudo-random code concept is quite esoteric, but it's an ingenious system that helps make GPS practical and relatively inexpensive to use. You might say that, in a way, it's the pseudo-random code that will allow GPS to become a basic "utility" that everyone can use.

We've already discussed how the pseudo-random code lets a receiver figure out the time difference between itself and a satellite, but that's only part of its function.

Another reason for the pseudo-random code is economic. And a good way to get a grip on how significant its contribution is, is to consider satellite TV. TV satellites broadcast
50

very powerful signals, and yet to receive them on earth we need large parabolic reflectors to concentrate the signal. Imagine how cumbersome GPS would be if every receiver needed a big dish. And what's more, TV satellites are in geosynchronous orbit, which means they're stationary in the sky. With GPS we'd not only need a big dish, but that dish would have to be able to alternate between four different moving targets. Quite a mechanical nightmare.

Pseudo-random code allows low power operation. The pseudo-random code eliminates the need for all that by using a tricky concept in information theory. Because of it, GPS signals can be very low power and still be received with antennae just a few inches across. In fact, GPS signals are so faint they don't register above the earth's inherent background radio noise.

The principle behind it all is quite sophisticated, but a layman's way of looking at it is this: Background radio noise is just a randomly varying string of electronic pulsations, as shown above.

Our pseudo-random code looks a lot like this with one important difference: we know the pattern of the fluctuations.

What if we compared a section of our pseudo-random code to a section of background noise and looked for areas where both were doing the same thing?

We can divide the signal up into time periods (called "chips" in GPS lingo) and then mark all the periods that match with "X"s.

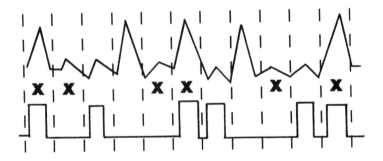

Since both signals are basically random patterns probability says that about half the time they'll match and half the time they won't.

So if we set up a scoring system and give ourselves a point when they match and subtract a point when they don't, we'd find that, over the long run, we'd end up with a final score of 0 because the "1"s would cancel out the "-1"s.

But now, if a GPS satellite starts sending a string of pulses in the same pattern as our
pseudo-random string, those signals, even
though they are weak, will tend to reinforce the
random background in the same pattern we're
using for our comparison. If we slide our
receiver's pseudo-random code around until it
lines up with the satellites, suddenly there will
be a lot more matches. And our score will
go up.

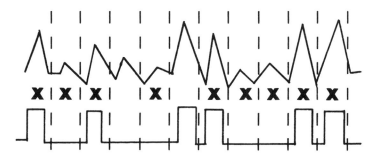

If we do the comparison over a large
number of time periods, we can make our score
bigger and bigger. The longer the period of
comparison, the bigger the number, and that acts
kind of like an "amplifier". We could choose a
comparison time that might give us a thousand
matches. And, since a comparison against just
random background noise would always yield a
score close to zero, this period would effectively
be amplifying our satellite signal by a thousand.

Now, this explanation is greatly simplified but the basic concept is significant. The pseudo-random code gives us a way of very clearly recognizing a very faint signal. It means the GPS satellites don't have to be very powerful (so they cost less) and it means that our receivers on the ground can get away with using very small antennae.

Why don't all satellites work this way? Why don't TV satellites do the same thing so we wouldn't have to have those giant dishes sprouting up all over the countryside? Well, the GPS signal has very little information in it. It's basically just a timing mark. TV signals, on the other hand, are loaded with information. Or as they say in the business, they're "very high bandwidth". The pseudo-random code principle relies on a comparison done over many cycles of a signal. This comparison is slow and cumbersome compared to a TV signal. The system just doesn't work fast enough to handle TV.

Pseudo-random code lets the DoD control access to the system

There are a couple of other reasons the system is based on a pseudo-random code. For one thing, it provides a way for the Department of Defense to control access to the satellite system. In a time of war, they could change the code and so prevent an enemy from using the system. Even in peacetime the DoD retains some "exclusivity" to the system. There are two separate forms of pseudo-random code, one called the "C/A code" and the other called the "P code". The C/A code is the one all the civilian receivers use. It's lower frequency than the P code, and so is thought by some to be less precise*. The P code can be encrypted so only military users are guaranteed access to it. In addition, the P code is almost impossible to jam.

The DoD may even degrade the current accuracy of the C/A code using an operational mode called "selective availability" or "S/A".

---

*Traditionally, the P code, which is superimposed on a carrier that is ten times the frequency of the C/A carrier, was thought to be an inherently more accurate signal to base GPS measurements on. But new receiver designs, for a variety of complicated reasons, are proving that there is practically no difference in the accuracy of measurements made with either C/A or P code.

S/A is essentially a method for artificially creating a significant clock error in the satellites. When implemented it is the largest source of error in the GPS system.

Another benefit of the pseudo-random code scheme is that all the satellites in the system can share the same frequency without interfering with each other. Each satellite has its own distinct pseudo-random code, so differentiating between them is only a matter of using the right code during the comparison process at the receiver. Since all transmissions are low power, no satellite overpowers any other.

Summary:

•Pseudo-random code is a way to unambiguously match a satellite signal to a receiver signal for timing purposes.

•The code allows the GPS system to work with very low power signals and small antennae.

•The code gives the DoD a way to control access to the system.

•The code allows all satellites to use one frequency.

7

Differential GPS –the ultimate in accuracy.

*G*PS is by far the most accurate global navigation system ever devised. But even its incredible accuracy can be boosted using a technique called "differential GPS". With it, GPS can achieve measurement accuracies of better than a meter. And that's bringing GPS into some surprising applications.

GPS for surveying Surveyors have been using GPS for several years now to calculate positions right down to the last centimeter! Their techniques are extensions of differential GPS. These ultra-precise measurements are usually based on at least fifteen minutes of GPS data collection at a stationary location, as well as the very precise knowledge of a reference point or "benchmark", and the use of a complex computer program.

With a GPS survey receiver, one surveyor can do the work of a whole team in a fraction of the time required by conventional techniques. No more does a crew have to hike over hill and dale to establish a line-of-sight connection to a known benchmark.

The new "kinematic" GPS survey systems now in development will be even more automatic. A surveyor merely walks to each point in the site he wants to stake and then pushes a button. The GPS receiver instantly records the stake's exact location.

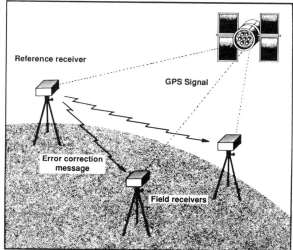

The secret to getting accuracies like these is based on the idea that if we put a GPS receiver on the ground in a *known* location, we can use it to figure out exactly what errors the satellite data contains. It acts like a static reference point. It can then transmit an error correction message to any other GPS receivers that are in the local area, and they can use that error message to correct their position solutions.

The concept works because the satellites are so high up that any errors measured by one receiver will be almost exactly the same for any other receiver in the same locale. Because of the simplicity of the GPS signal, this single correction factor, in effect, takes care of all the possible errors in the system, whether they're from receiver clocks, the satellite clocks, the satellite's position, or ionospheric and atmospheric delays.

The error message that the reference receiver sends to the other receivers can take a couple of forms. The main technique is for the error message to be sent by telemetry to the other receivers which then process that message, along with the position data calculated, to determine a converted position.

Summary:

•Differential GPS measurements can be much more accurate than standard GPS measurements.

•A receiver placed at a known location calculates the combined error in the satellite range data.

•That correction can be applied to all other receivers in the same locale, to eliminate virtually all error in their measurements.

Selecting a GPS receiver.

*G*PS will soon be a basic utility that almost everyone will use in one way or another.   It's a system with tremendous potential and a wide variety of possible uses.   Getting just the right equipment for your particular use requires a careful analysis of how you'll be using the receiver, what kind of information you need from it and what your budget will allow.

Some of the questions you should consider before making a decision are:

• Do you just need an occasional position fix or do you need something that will allow accurate steering?

• Do you need to accurately measure your velocity — as you might when you're tuning the performance of a racing yacht or evaluating engine performance?

- Is economy more important than accuracy?

- Is power consumption an important factor?

- Will the receiver have to operate in high dynamic conditions, experiencing accelerations and high velocities?

With so many receivers on the market it may be useful to outline the major types of receivers available, their design philosophies, and some of their advantages and disadvantages.

The two broad groups of receivers are those that can track four or more satellites simultaneously, and those that sequence between the satellites. And within each category there are a variety of subspecies:

Sequencing Receivers All GPS receivers must receive information from at least four satellites to calculate an accurate position. Sequencing receivers use a single channel and move it from one satellite to the next to gather this data. They usually have less circuitry so they're cheaper and they consume less power. Unfortunately the sequencing can interrupt positioning and can limit their overall accuracy.

Within this group there are "Starved-Power" Single-Channel Receivers, Single-Channel Receivers, Two-Channel Receivers, and the older Fast-Multiplexing, Single-Channel receivers.

Starved-power, Single Channel Receivers These devices are geared for portability and so are usually designed to run off small batteries. To limit power consumption they may only take a position reading once or twice a minute and turn themselves off in between.

For applications like a personal positioner for hikers or day sailing in small boats without batteries, they're the perfect compromise. Their accuracy is probably better than most LORANs and they work anywhere in the world.

Their main disadvantage is degraded accuracy, limited interfacing and their inability to measure velocity with any precision. Since the system shuts off between measurements it cannot maintain the continuity required to calculate accurate velocity. And because such units are usually outfitted with low-power reference clock circuits (because the clock must remain on at all times) their clocks are not as accurate.

Single Channel Receivers Like the receivers above, these systems use a single channel to do all satellite ranging. But unlike those above, the standard single-channel receiver is not limited by power and so can remain on continuously.

This means that they can be a bit more accurate and can measure velocity as long as there are no significant accelerations or course changes. Since their only channel must be used for receiving satellite data messages as well as for performing ranging calculations, they cannot be used for continuous positioning.

In addition, for technical reasons, the instability of the receiver's clock directly affects the accuracy of its velocity measurements. Some low cost receivers use cheap clocks in an effort to drive cost down, and the result is velocity numbers you can't trust.

Fast-multiplexing, Single Channel Receivers This design is very similar to the slow sequencing single channel receivers mentioned above, but it moves from satellite to satellite much faster. The advantage is that it can actually make ranging measurements while it's also monitoring a satellite's data message. So it can function continuously. It's also less sensitive to clock inaccuracies.

Unfortunately this approach requires more complex circuitry and ends up costing as much as a two-channel sequencing receiver, which is much more flexible and more accurate.

Two-channel Sequencing Receivers

Adding a second channel to a GPS receiver increases its capabilities significantly. For one thing it immediately doubles the system's inherent signal-to-noise ratio. That means it can lock on to signals under more adverse conditions, and can track satellites closer to the horizon.

Since one channel can be continuously monitoring positioning data while the other is busy acquiring the next satellite, a two channel receiver never has to interrupt its navigation functions. And velocity measurements can be much more precise. In fact, a good two-channel receiver can use a computation strategy that will cancel out any inaccuracies the receiver's clock could add to velocity calculations.

The disadvantage of a two-channel design is that it usually will cost more to build and may use more power. Interestingly, some modern receivers make such extensive use of large-scale integrated circuits that for them the incremental cost of adding a second channel is insignificant relative to the cost of a good clock.

Even so, two-channel receivers are usually more expensive than their single channel counterparts. This stems from the fact that users who want the accuracy and continuous function of a two-channel receiver usually also want a more robust package and more sophisticated controls and displays.

Continuous Receivers Receivers that can monitor four or more satellites simultaneously can give instantaneous position and velocity. This can be valuable in high-dynamic or high-accuracy applications, so they're often used for surveying and scientific purposes. You'll see them in 4, 6, 8 and even 10 and 12 channel configurations.

Besides the obvious advantage of being able to continuously measure a position, these multi-channel receivers can also eliminate the GDOP problem. Instead of relying on a calculation of which four satellites are positioned for the best fix, some of these systems track all the satellites in view, to get the absolute minimum GDOP.

With four channels, a receiver can double the signal-to-noise ratio of a two-channel receiver and quadruple that of a single-channel system. And by comparing channels to each other, it can calibrate out any interchannel biases that could affect accuracy.

Naturally, the drawbacks of these kinds of systems are their size, cost and power consumption.

Other considerations Beyond the advantages and disadvantages of specific architectures there are some additional considerations to take into account as you select a system.

Some newer systems are achieving unprecedented accuracies by tracking both the pseudo-random code and its carrier frequency. Called "carrier-aided tracking", this system makes it possible for the receiver to resolve, with great precision, exactly where the "edge" of the pseudo-random code falls. And that means more precise timing measurements, which, in turn, translates into better positioning.

There are still some receivers that need to be told their approximate position and the approximate time before they can start their calculations. Good receivers can start cold and establish their position anywhere. It's often called an "anywhere fix."

Another thing to consider when buying a receiver is its user interface. Some units give latitude and longitude and not much more. Some are very difficult to use and cannot be connected to other instruments or computers.

And of course, reliability is another big factor to consider with any instrument that will be taken out to sea or into remote field locations. Power usage, and the heat that goes with it, are important indicators to watch. Statistics show that failure rates double for every seven degrees of increased temperature.

Today's more sophisticated receivers add a lot of value to the basic GPS information, processing it in very complex ways. They often present it on high-resolution displays. One receiver even displays your position right on a digitized chart.

So while all receivers deal with the same GPS data, they use it in very different ways. They can use that data to help you make navigation and positioning decisions that go well beyond just latitude and longitude.

Receiver Shopping Tip

A quick way to test the accuracy of a receiver is to watch its readings for both position and velocity while the unit is stationary.

A good receiver will change readings very little, if at all. A poor system's readings will fluctuate all over the place.

Beware: Some manufacturers mask their system's performance by programming their machines to indicate zero when its velocity falls below one knot.

Glossary of GPS terms.

Anywhere fix the ability of a receiver to start position calculations without being given an approximate location and approximate time.

Bandwidth the range of frequencies in a signal.

C/A code the standard (Course/Acquisition) GPS code — a sequence of 1023 pseudo-random, binary, biphase modulations on the GPS carrier at a chip rate of 1.023 MHz. Also known as the "civilian code."

Carrier a signal that can be varied from a known reference by modulation.

Carrier-aided tracking a signal processing strategy that uses the GPS carrier signal to achieve an exact lock on the pseudo random code. More accurate than standard approach.

Carrier frequency the frequency of the unmodulated fundamental output of a radio transmitter.

Channel a channel of a GPS receiver consists of the circuitry necessary to tune the signal from a single GPS satellite.

Chip the transition time for individual bits in the pseudo-random sequence. Also, an integrated circuit.

Clock bias the difference between the clock's indicated time and true universal time.

Control segment a world-wide network of GPS monitoring and control stations that ensure the accuracy of satellite positions and their clocks.

Cycle slip a discontinuity in the measured carrier beat phase resulting from a temporary loss-of-lock in the carrier tracking loop of a GPS receiver.

Data message   a message included in the GPS signal which reports the satellite's location, clock corrections and health. Included is rough information on the other satellites in the constellation.

Differential positioning   precise measurement of the relative positions of two receivers tracking the same GPS signals.

Dilution of Precision   the multiplicative factor that modifies ranging error. It is caused solely by the geometry between the user and his set of satellites. Known as DOP or GDOP.

Doppler-aiding   a signal processing strategy that uses a measured doppler shift to help the receiver smoothly track the GPS signal. Allows more precise velocity and position measurement.

Doppler shift   the apparent change in the frequency of a signal caused by the relative motion of the transmitter and receiver.

Ephemeris   the predictions of current satellite position that are transmitted to the user in the data message.

Fast-multiplexing channel a single channel which rapidly samples a number of satellite ranges. "Fast" means that the switching time is suffficiently fast (2 to 5 milliseconds) to recover the data message.

Frequency band a particular range of frequencies.

Frequency spectrum the distribution of signal amplitudes as a function of frequency.

Geometric Dilution of Precision (GDOP) see Dilution of Precision.

Handover word the word in the GPS message that contains synchronization information for the transfer of tracking from the C/A to P code.

Ionosphere the band of charged particles 80 to 120 miles above the earth's surface.

Ionospheric refraction the change in the propagation speed of a signal as it passes through the ionosphere.

L-band   the group of radio frequencies extending from 390MHz to 1550MHz. The GPS carrier frequencies (1227.6MHz and 1575.42MHz) are in the L band.

Multipath error   errors caused by the interference of a signal that has reached the receiver antenna by two or more different paths. Usually caused by one path being bounced or reflected.

Multi-channel receiver   a GPS receiver that can simultaneously track more than one satellite signal.

Multiplexing channel   a channel of a GPS receiver that can be sequenced through a number of satellite signals.

P-code   the Precise or Protected code. A very long sequence of pseudo-random binary biphase modulations on the GPS carrier at a chip rate of 10.23 MHz which repeats about every 267 days. Each one week segment of this code is unique to one GPS satellite and is reset each week.

Precise Positioning Service (PPS)   the most accurate dynamic positioning possible with GPS, based on the dual frequency P-code.

74

Pseudolite a ground-based differential GPS receiver which transmits a signal like that of an actual GPS satellite and can be used for ranging. The data portion of the signal contains the differential corrections that can be used by other receivers to correct for GPS errors.

Pseudo-random code a signal with random-noise like properties. It is a very complicated but repeated pattern of 1's and 0's.

Pseudorange a distance measurement based on the correlation of a satellite transmitted code and the local receiver's reference code, that has not been corrected for errors in synchronization between the transmitter's clock and the receiver's clock.

Satellite constellation the arrangement in space of a set of satellites.

Space segment the part of the whole GPS system that includes the satellites and the launch vehicles.

Spread spectrum a system in which the transmitted signal is spread over a frequency band much wider than the minimum bandwidth needed to transmit the information being sent. For GPS, this is done by modulating the carrier with a pseudo-random code.

Standard positioning service (SPS) the normal civilian positioning accuracy obtained by using the single frequency C/A code.

Static positioning location determination when the receiver's antenna is presumed to be stationary in the earth.   This allows the use of various averaging techniques that improve accuracy by factors of over 1000.

User interface the way a receiver conveys information to the person using it. The controls and displays.

User segment the part of the whole GPS system that includes the receivers of GPS signals.